10.95

ANDREW LLOYD WEBBER
SHOWSTOPPERS
Playalong *for* Clarinet

Wise Publications
part of The Music Sales Group
London/New York/Paris/Sydney/Copenhagen/Berlin/Madrid/Tokyo

Published by
Wise Publications
8/9 Frith Street, London W1D 3JB, England.

Exclusive Distributors:
Music Sales Limited
Distribution Centre, Newmarket Road, Bury St. Edmunds,
Suffolk IP33 3YB England.
Music Sales Pty Limited
120 Rothschild Avenue, Rosebery, NSW 2018, Australia.

Order No. AM91937
ISBN 0-7119-4053-3
This book © Copyright 2005 by Wise Publications.

Compiled by Nick Crispin.
Edited by Christopher Hussey and Rebecca Taylor.
Music arranged by Quentin Thomas.
Music processed by Camden Music.
Cover photography by George Taylor.
Printed in Great Britain.

CD recorded, mixed and mastered by Jonas Persson and John Rose.
Clarinet played by John Whelan.
Backing tracks:
'As If We Never Said Goodbye', 'Love Changes Everything', 'The Phantom Of The Opera',
'Superstar' and 'Whistle Down The Wind' arranged by Danny G.
'Close Every Door' and 'Pie Jesu' arranged by John Maul.
'Don't Cry For Me Argentina' and 'Memory' arranged by Paul Honey.
'Unexpected Song' arranged by Jeff Leach.

Your Guarantee of Quality:
As publishers, we strive to produce every book to
the highest commercial standards.
The music has been freshly engraved and the book has been
carefully designed to minimise awkward page turns and
to make playing from it a real pleasure.
Particular care has been given to specifying acid-free, neutral-sized
paper made from pulps which have not been elemental chlorine bleached.
This pulp is from farmed sustainable forests and was
produced with special regard for the environment.
Throughout, the printing and binding have been planned to
ensure a sturdy, attractive publication which should give years of enjoyment.
If your copy fails to meet our high standards,
please inform us and we will gladly replace it.

www.musicsales.com

Clarinet Fingering Chart

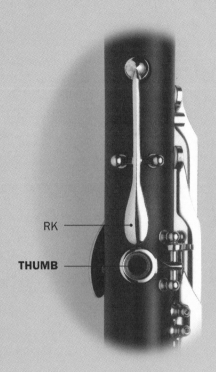

RK

THUMB

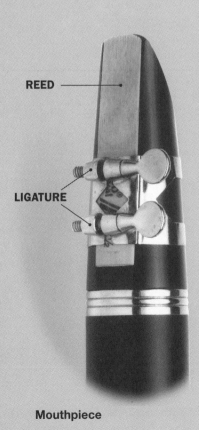

REED

LIGATURE

Mouthpiece

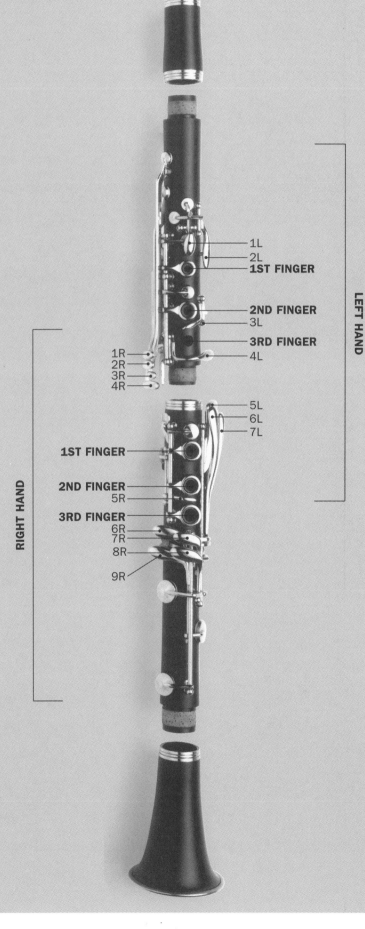

LEFT HAND

1L
2L
1ST FINGER

2ND FINGER
3L
3RD FINGER
1R
2R
4L
3R
4R

5L
6L
7L

RIGHT HAND

1ST FINGER

2ND FINGER
5R

3RD FINGER
6R
7R
8R
9R

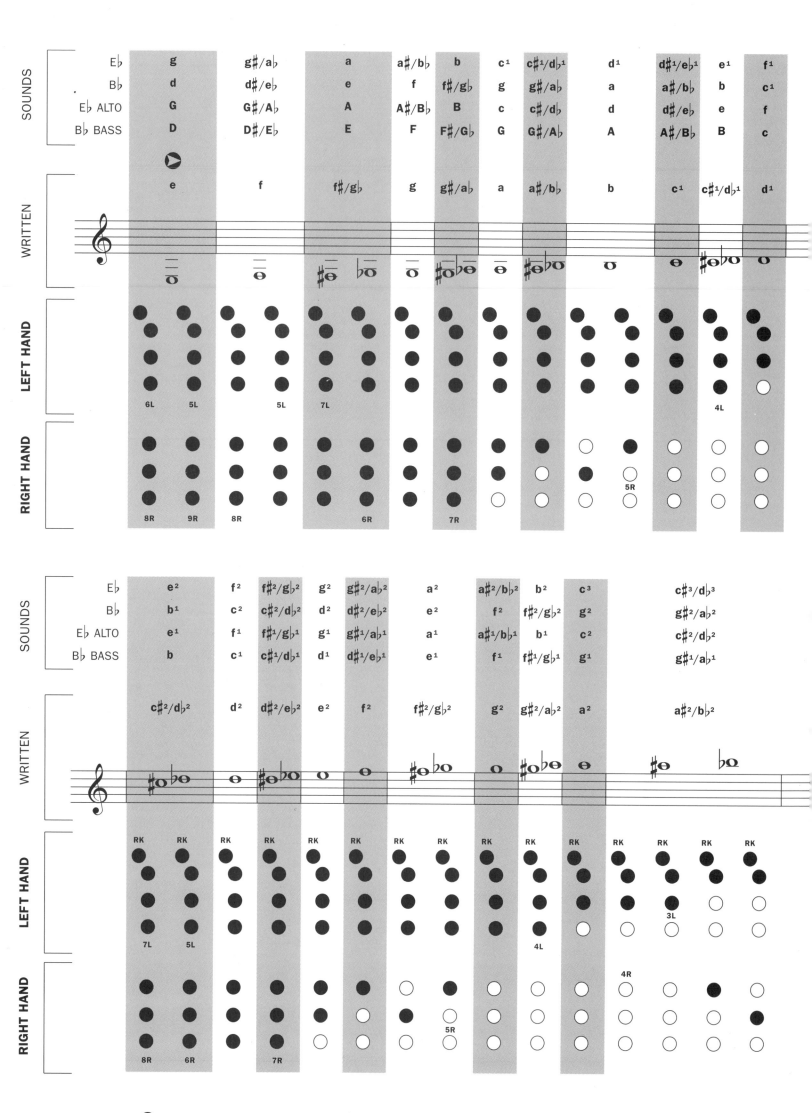

Indicates the lower limit of the best playing range for E♭, B♭, E♭ Alto and B♭ Bass Clarinets

Indicates the upper limit of the best playing range for E♭ and B♭ Clarinets

Indicates the upper limit of the best playing range for E♭ Alto and B♭ Bass Clarinets

As If We Never Said Goodbye

Music by Andrew Lloyd Webber
Words by Don Black & Christopher Hampton

Moderato

rit.

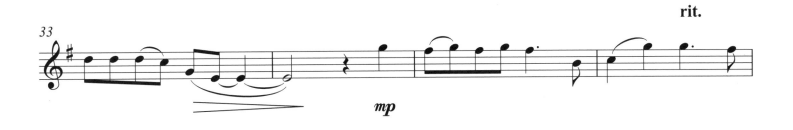

a tempo   **piu mosso**

molto allargando

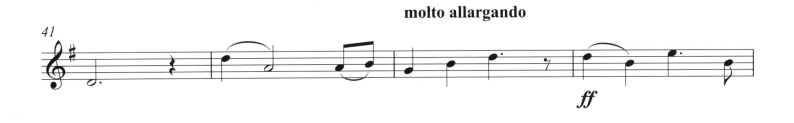

a tempo

molto   *p*

f

rall.   **Slow**

ff

Close Every Door

Music by Andrew Lloyd Webber
Words by Tim Rice

Espressivo

rit.   a tempo

rit.

a tempo

mf

rall.   **a tempo**

p

mf   *p*   *mf*   *p*

molto rall.

11

Love Changes Everything

Music by Andrew Lloyd Webber
Words by Don Black & Charles Hart

Memory

Music by Andrew Lloyd Webber
Words by Trevor Nunn after T.S.Eliot

The Phantom Of The Opera

Music by Andrew Lloyd Webber
Words by Charles Hart

Allegro vivace

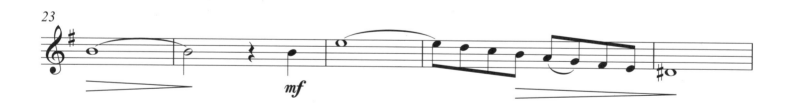

16

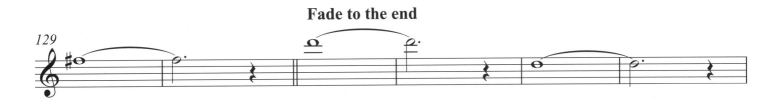

Fade to the end

Pie Jesu

Music by Andrew Lloyd Webber

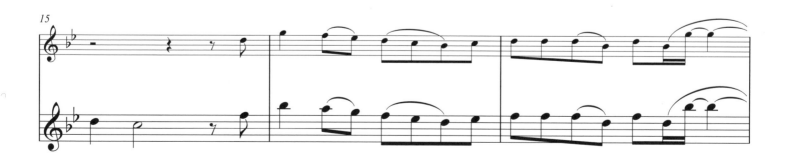

Don't Cry For Me Argentina

Music by Andrew Lloyd Webber
Words by Tim Rice

Slowly

Slow tango feel

mp

p

mp

poco rall.   **Slower**

p

Tempo 1º

mf

mp

Slower and freely

p

rit.

Refrain grandioso

f

molto
allargando

a tempo

mp

Superstar

Music by Andrew Lloyd Webber
Words by Tim Rice

Repeat 2 times and fade towards end

Unexpected Song

Music by Andrew Lloyd Webber
Words by Don Black

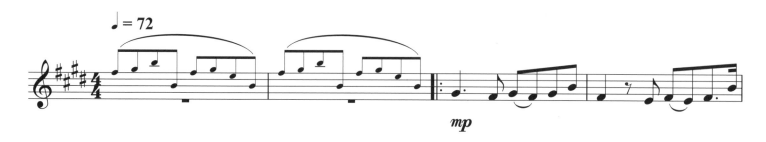

rall.   Slower

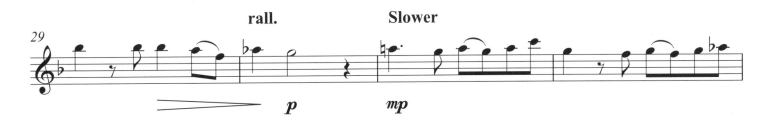

Whistle Down The Wind

Music by Andrew Lloyd Webber
Words by Jim Steinman

Moderato con moto

molto allargando   a tempo, broadly

rall.

11/06 (60395)